A FIERCE FLOURISHING

Mothers of Preschoolers

This workbook has been published as an exclusive Membership Benefit for MOPS International, Mothers of Preschoolers, www.mops.org

First Distribution, 2015

MOPS International
Publishing, attn: Liz Sagaser
2370 South Trenton Way
Denver, CO 80231

888.910.6677
lsagaser@mops.org
www.mops.org

I hope you will go out and **let stories happen to you** and that you will work them *water them with your blood and tears* & your laughter till they bloom *till you yourself burst into bloom*

Clarissa Pinkola Estes

TABLE *of* CONTENTS

Celebrate Lavishly

Embrace Rest

Noticing Goodness

A QUICK NOTE

Dear Mom,

It's such a privilege to welcome you to *A Fierce Flourishing*, our mom workbook created expressly for you, written by other moms who know what being a mom is all about. At MOPS we know there is nothing more important than being a mom. We also know it's hard. It's real. It's exhilarating to the point it takes our breath away, and it's oh so worth it. That's what *A Fierce Flourishing* is all about.

I will be simply direct and say we won't waste your time in the following pages, nor will we shy away from subjects that are sometimes hard to talk about. The imperfectness of being a mom. The feelings of inadequacy and failure. The scary-hard edges of relationships that mystify us in their elusiveness. But we'll also dive head first into celebrating the raw beauty that comes from honest acknowledgement and a refusal to deny or pretend. The land where real moms live is the soil of these pages.

We know you fell crazy in love with your kids the moment they burst on the scene (or sometime thereafter), but we also understand the accompanying moments of frustration and anxiety and questions. We know you feel moments of anger and resentment and selfishness. We live those moments, too; we understand.

I invite you to bring your whole self to this book, whether you read it alone or with a friend. Don't hide from what God might be trying to say to you, or the places where he is wooing your heart. Allow yourself to go deeper. Get honest. Don't hide. Open your heart to things both joyous and painful, and don't turn away. It is in the spaces where God stirs us most deeply that he has the most to say. Allow him to speak. Then listen.

I want to say thanks to the wonderful moms who created this book. They bare themselves openly, willingly – because they know you are worth it. They ask nothing in return except your open acceptance and your willingness to allow your soul to resonate.

I love you deeply,
Sherry Surratt
MOPS International CEO & President

INTRODUCTION

Please consider this book a campfire set aflame in your honor – a gathering place that draws us in toward warmth and conversation. Sometimes we will be mesmerized by the swirling and flickering of the magnificent light; we'll be compelled to sit quietly beside one another as we take it all in. Other times the air will be filled with raucous laughter as we struggle to find our breath amidst the honesty and goodness of being with friends. Our time together in this book will remind us that we were meant to enjoy life – not be drowned by it. Huddled together around a common source of heat and light, may we find healing and be reacquainted with joyful living.

This year at MOPS we have decided that we want to experience life in all its glittering glory, and to invite all of our sisters to do the same. So here is what we are going to do: We are going to Embrace Rest, Notice Goodness and Celebrate Lavishly – together.

Embrace Rest. This is the year to let go of exhaustion as a status symbol and productivity as a measure of worth. What if one of the most life-giving activities that will contribute to our flourishing is welcoming rhythms of rest and play into our lives? Creating healthy life rhythms is one way we nourish the weary spots in our soul.

Notice Goodness. Could it be possible that we don't need new things, but rather new eyes to see what we already have? What if we regained our sense of vision and developed an acute resolve to find hope in the cracks and mires of the mundane? Noticing what is good gives us the gift of perspective, and reminds us that the sacred is closer than we think.

Celebrate Lavishly. Celebrating breathes life into our days. Could it be that commemorating moments might help us to become more alive, to remember what is good and become masterful at recognizing it? How would life change if we regularly invited friends into our stolen moments with uninhibited dancing and the best food, while gathered around the biggest table with the deepest conversations? Lavish celebrations can be sacred markers that help remind us who we are.

We become more ourselves when we celebrate, rest and notice... and that looks a lot like flourishing. But this flourishing isn't the precious or exhausting kind.

This is a fierce flourishing. It is a deep in your guts experience of gratitude and hope that compels you to raise your hands and dance freer than you ever have before. It is a fierce protection of your most important moments, an invitation to rest and an opportunity to enjoy the people who are right in front of you.

So, may these written words spark a revival of hope deep in the weary parts of your bones. May you reach your hands toward the warmth of words that are flickering and dancing across these pages, and may you find the forgotten parts of your soul that are reemerging as you journey toward your own fierce flourishing.

Chapter One

FAMILY

• • • • • • • • • • • • • • • Emily T. Wierenga • • • • • • • • • • • • • •

"Love is the flower you've got to let grow"
- John Lennon

We were in a garden of peonies, bursting pink and rose and ivory on dozens of bushes – and the air smelled like my grandmother's perfume. I was leaning over the blossoms even as my three-year-old fingered their soft petals and my mother in law, standing there, pointed to a blossom that hadn't opened yet, rolled tight into a pink ball; tiny ants crawled across its surface.

"Peonies can't open without the ants," my mother in law said. "See how they're moving across the surface of the blossom? They're opening it so that it can bloom."

I just stared as these tiny ants, who appeared to be doing nothing, worked the miracle of unfolding one of earth's most extravagant flowers.

And it reminded me of us, as mothers, working tirelessly each day so that one day, our children might blossom.

As mothers we live largely in the hidden years, in the shadows of the unfolded bloom. We spend hours doing tiny, mundane things like wiping noses and bottoms and tables and chairs and cupboards and floors, and getting on our hands and knees to look into the eyes of a child and disciplining and comforting, potty training and bathtub-scrubbing, mountains of laundry-folding and us, on the couch, crying into a mug of coffee because today of all days, the kids refuse to nap.

And then we walk wearily down the stairs and pick those little ones up and rock them and read them the same stories, over and over, until it's time to make supper.

And that's when we realize we're still in our pajamas.

Life, for a mom, is largely secret and unseen. We wonder if anyone cares. Does any of this count toward anything at all?

But God sees. And there is nothing that delights him more than love done in secret.

We live in a world that says it doesn't matter if no one witnesses it—that unless it's recorded on YouTube or tweeted or made into a status or posted on a blog, it doesn't count.

But we also live in a world that is disillusioned by fame and hungry for unannounced sacrifice.

I recently listened to a talk by a former atheist who now speaks about the life of Christ and all of the years the Bible doesn't talk about—the "hidden years" she calls them, leading up to his ministry.

God didn't love Jesus just because of the way he served him in public.

He loved him because of the way he served him in private.

For all of the ways he served his Father in the quiet of the thirty years prior to his ministry. All of the small, ordinary choices he made as a carpenter – the ant crawling across the bloom of the flower – believing one day its work would be honored, but content until then to keep working at what it has been called to do. As mothers we have been called to serve our families. To do those small, unseen things that don't get a lot of praise or exclamation, that leave us some days weeping into our coffee for the longing to be noticed.

But oh, how your Father notices.

And may you hear, as Jesus did, when he emerged from the water prior to starting any kind of ministry, God's voice declaring proudly from heaven, "This is my daughter, with whom I am well pleased."

Even as the peony unfolds.

Is it hard to believe that the work you do around the house and with your kids matters? Why/why not?

What sorts of activities/habits make it harder to value the quiet, secret things? Do you make a habit of comparing your life to that of others online? Would you be willing to replace this activity with one that is more affirming, like going for a walk or reading a good book?

What are ways that you can invite celebration into the most ordinary of days? Are you open to having "pajama day" with your kids, or having dessert for supper, or spending the morning snuggling instead of cleaning the bathroom?

Are there hobbies that you can pursue when your kids are asleep which will remind you of life beyond diapers and aprons?

What have you been taught, over your life, about the role of the mother/ wife? How much truth is in this teaching, and which values/views need to be reshaped?

Chapter Two

FEASTING

• • • • • • • • • • • • • • • • Mandy Arioto • • • • • • • • • • • • • • • •

"Grace is the celebration of life, relentlessly hounding all the non-celebrants in the world. It is a floating, cosmic bash shouting its way through the streets of the universe, flinging the sweetness of its cassations to every window, pounding at every door in a hilarity beyond all liking and happening, until the prodigals come out at last and dance, and the elder brothers finally take their fingers out of their ears."
— Robert Farrar Capon

So a couple of things happened this week that I should probably tell you about. The first is that I complimented a woman at the grocery store on the ugly Christmas sweater she was obviously sporting for an ugly sweater party – only to find out that she wasn't heading to any such party. She just thought it was a great holiday sweater. Second, when someone asked my daughter what her favorite meal that I make was, she answered, "Cereal." And one more thing? On top of all of this, I realized that I have become my mother.

The realization that I have become my mother happened in the hallowed halls of Trader Joe's. As I was shopping for the usuals (the aforementioned cereal, among other things), one of the best songs from the 90's came on, and I was compelled to dance in the aisles. My kids were with me and were completely mortified. But when 'Play That Funky Music' comes on? I am going to dance. It might not have been so terrible for my precious and embarrassed children except for the fact that a teenage boy stocking shelves saw my amazing dance moves, grabbed my hand, and proceeded to spin me around the aisle. Bless his heart. My children will someday write about this slice of family life with less enthusiasm than I had in the moment. Or maybe they'll save this one for therapy...

It was at this very moment – twirling through the juice aisle of Trader Joe's – that I realized I was my mother. Vivid memories of my mom dancing through stores to her favorite songs flashed through my mind, and I had to laugh. I actually wear this "I am becoming my Mother" badge with honor. I couldn't be prouder to share so many qualities with the best woman I know, but there are still a few elusive qualities of hers that I am working on mastering. Like her ability to turn any meal into a feast, and any moment into an experience.

I like moments. There is so much potential in every single one.

Have you ever had a moment where you lose sense of time? I remember as a kid playing outside and not even realizing it was getting dark. I was so consumed by the fun of the game that the darkness didn't matter. Or I think about two years ago, dancing at Drea and Hal's wedding in Brooklyn and being so consumed by the love of everyone in the room that I wanted to stay on that dance floor all night. It's the wide eyed, fully present, never-want-it-to-end moments that make life worthwhile.

I heard it said once that this sense of timelessness is a prophetic groaning of heaven. I really like that idea. I also like the idea that we can slow time down and fit more life into our moments. It isn't about living in timelessness all the time, because life will push back with obligations. But we can find those cracks when the spiritual, emotional and physical all come together. A sense of timeless delight where what is happening inside and what is happening outside and all around us are completely synched up for a brief moment. In my frame of reference this is an experience of the sacred.

In Celtic spirituality they have a term for this phenomena. They call it liminal space: Where the line between earth and heaven is so thin, it is hard to tell where one ends and the other begins.

I think another word for this experience is feasting.

My understanding of feasting is less about food and more about inviting timelessness into our lives. It seems to me like this is something we could all use more of.

I have come to learn that feasting has three main attributes:
Noticing Goodness
Lavish Celebration
Extreme Generosity

Noticing goodness is what sparks feasting. It is an intentional slowing down so we can be more in tune with the beauty that is all around us, waiting to be experienced. It is the belly laughs coming from the dark bedrooms where kids should be fast asleep, but are whispering silliness to one another. It is the smell of fresh laundry and the bounty of a full fridge. It is everyday mundaneness that is glittering before our very eyes – if only we choose to pay attention to it.
Lavish celebration is about generosity and excess. I believe that there is a time

for everything. There is a time for less. For less eating, less having, less spending. In these moments of fasting, we learn we can survive on less of everything and still be ok. There is also a time for feasting. And feasting isn't a time for moderation. It is a time for celebrating big. For laughing too loudly and eating decadent foods and savoring friendship and inviting everyone in. It is sharing our excess with the people around us and looking back at God with hearts *so full of gratitude* that we have no choice but to express it.

This sharing is where the generosity comes in. It is an act of hospitality. It is feasting on behalf of others successes. It means showing up and matching the celebratory attitude at play, rather than sulking and being too cool to shake it on the dance floor.

Sometimes feasting feels like too much, so we hold back and never really experience the wild and free expressions of delight we have inside. What are these things that keep us from feasting? I have come to believe it comes down to two things: shame and control.

In our culture we have gotten really comfortable with being busy. Like "having too much to do" is a virtue to be admired. We have a work ethic that has been drilled into our subconscious and are told we are only valuable when we are productive. This means that when we do embrace moments of feasting, we often feel shame that we aren't being productive or aren't using our resources wisely.

For others of us, shame is triggered by our spirituality. We feel less spiritual if we celebrate lavishly. In fact for many of us in the west, our spirituality is esteemed for being self-contained, prudent and internal. Our relationship with God tends to be more intellectual and less emotional. An interesting result of this type of thinking is that many religious people are dry and boring and hard to be around. I believe our view of what is spiritual is far too small. And frankly? Far too boring. Dialogue can be as spiritual as silence, dancing can be as spiritual as kneeling and feasting can be as spiritual as fasting. When we remember that Jesus' first miracle was turning water into wine, that he shared meals with whores and raged at the overly pious, I think we have to reconsider our understanding of holiness.

Another thing that triggers our shame response is control. When we let our hair down and celebrate, sometimes we start to feel like we are being too much, too out of control, laughing too loudly, indulging too extravagantly. Or we diminish our delight so that we appear in control or don't embarrass ourselves. The issue with this way of being is that an experience of timelessness rarely happens when we are collected and in control, and feasting never happens just in our heads. *Delight isn't complete until it is expressed.*

I love people who can be free with their delight. They hug longer than everyone else, they sing louder and cry more freely. They tell everyone around them just how much they love them, and never worry about looking like they are in control. They are free to feast. And I believe that God delights in our delight.

So what does this look like in your life? It would be presumptuous of me to tell you what feasting looks like for you. I tell a few stories about times where I have experienced feasting that healed parts of my soul in the video that goes with this chapter. If you don't have a chance to see it in your MOPS group, call me and I will share with you about them. My cell phone number is 951.719.7440. I may not answer it right away but leave me a message I and I will call you back, because I believe feasting has to go public.

We will be better humans when we learn to celebrate well. However feasting takes shape in your life, may it be an accumulation of moments that give us all glimpses of God's kingdom that he likens to a huge party. A party whose music is already echoing throughout heaven and this world – and over the loud speakers at Trader Joe's. May we hear it and experience feasting as never before. Don't wait until you think you have something to celebrate. You have something to celebrate now. *Ask for the eyes to see it.*

May we bring feasting wherever we go by making moments into celebrations and crumbs into feasts. May we flourish deeply as we delight in the pleasures of being alive. So friends: savor meals, laugh enough – or even too much, and remind yourself to live a little, because feasting is good not only for our own souls, but the world as well. When we feast it brings the world glimpses of goodness, and that makes us all a little warmer and a little kinder. Until further notice: celebrate everything, share stories and meals, be lavish in your feasting and dance until something hurts.

• • • • • • • • • • • • • *Reflection Questions* • • • • • • • • • • • •

When is the last time you celebrated lavishly?

What inhibits you from living in the moment and laughing out loud?

Do you feel closest to God in quiet moments, or in the no-holds-barred moments of your life? Why?

If no one was watching or listening, how would you express delight?

What is one thing you can do this week to celebrate lavishly, and who can you invite to the feast?

Chapter Three

SEXUALITY

• • • • • • • • • • • • • • • Emily T. Wierenga • • • • • • • • • • • • • • •

"The real act of marriage takes place in the heart, not in the ballroom or church or synagogue. It's a choice you make - not just on your wedding day, but over and over again - and that choice is reflected in the way you treat your husband or wife."
- Barbara de Angelis

We borrowed my aunt's cabin, by the water.

We arrived late with a bottle of wine and I stepped on the back of my wedding dress as we crossed the threshold.

I didn't see anything but the bed, with its nicely folded corners and my new husband already in his boxers and grabbing us goblets from the kitchen cupboard.

I leaned against the wall, drinking the wine, in white, and *we were 23-year-old virgins who'd never seen each other naked, had only felt each other's skin, and I couldn't unzip my dress.*

I stalled, pulling out bobby pins. He helped me; we made a tidy pile of pins and then he asked if he could help me with my zipper.

And I asked him if he wanted another glass of wine.

It wasn't that I didn't want to make love with him.

It's that I didn't want him to see me. All of me.

I didn't want him to see my crooked, scoliosis-spine; the pear shape of my maiden hips and the flat front of my chest which I used to stuff with Kleenex to fill in the gaps of high school. But more than that, I didn't want him to see my heart beating wildly through that flat chest, pounding for fear of him laughing, or worse – saying nothing – just turning away in disappointment.

We were each other's first, and what if I wasn't enough for my husband's years of patient waiting?

He deserves so much more, I convinced myself, and even as he unzipped the back of my dress and it fell around my feet like a crumpled carnation, my spirits fell too – and I snuck between the sheets and shivered.

He came to the other side of the bed, drew me close, pulled the sheets from my uneven shoulders and kissed them one by one. He kissed the freckles on my nose, looked into my eyes and said, "You're beautiful."

Genesis talks about Adam and Eve being naked and unashamed before the fall, before the curse of humanity, and I long for this freedom to be unashamed before my husband. Before the one who's seen all of my flaws and loves me anyway, who calls me beautiful. Yet, in spite of it being 11 years and three children later – my body born and torn with flesh – I still find myself hiding behind fleecy pajamas.

Why does it feel more comfortable to hide?

Why is it so hard to believe we are enough – not because we have the perfect body, whatever that looks like (I'm beginning to think it looks "dinged and dented" as Rachel Jankovic says in Loving the Little Years) but because *love makes us enough?* The love of a Savior whose own body hung broken and bruised so we could once again be whole? Naked and unashamed?

It's a slow act of humility. Like the soft fall of a wedding dress.

When I stand before him now with stretch marks lacing my stomach and my front somehow flatter than before, I don't look down. Instead, I look into my husband's eyes and in them, I see the truth about who I am. Because really, we're our own worst enemies, ladies. We are the ones who don't like ourselves. Our husbands beg us come as we are; they just want to feel us in their arms, trusting them. Trusting the love they have for us.

And it's in this naked place that we find it.

Grace.

Do you find it easy to get naked in front of your husband? Why/why not? What would make it easier?

Have you always struggled with a sense of shame when it comes to your body? If so, when did it start, and why?

What are some ways you can practice being naked and unashamed? Are you open to saying "Thank You" to your body in the mirror for all the ways it's carried you through the years?

What are some lies you believe about your self-worth and value which have ingrained themselves in your skin? How can you undo those lies and replace them with the truth about who you are: Cherished, Delighted In, Accepted, and Lovable?

Communication is a key to unlocking intimacy in the bedroom. What are some ways you and your husband can improve upon your communication?

Chapter Four

CREATIVITY & PLAY

• • • • • • • • • • • • • • • • • • • Lori Lara • • • • • • • • • • • • • • • • • • •

"Play is the highest form of research... Imagination is more important than knowledge. Knowledge is limited. Imagination encircles the world." — Albert Einstein

Many of us grew up believing there are two kinds of people in the world: the artists, and the rest of us who tried desperately to cover up our sad attempts at drawing in grade school. It was immediately clear my stick-figure sketches would never see the clean white light of an art gallery. So, even though I continually wrote poems and essays about life as I grew older, I didn't consider myself a creative person. I lived with the "non-artist" stamp on my psyche.

But when I fell in love with photography in college (a class I took only to fulfill my art requirement), I learned drawing was just one creative art form; there are countless others.

We might not all be Picassos, Beethovens or Pinterest moms, but everyone has a creative genius. Whether we are a doctor, scientist, architect, actor, dancer, painter, homemaker, business person or philanthropist, God has given each of us a unique way of seeing life. And when we allow our minds to roam freely within our imaginations and fields of interest, we bring beauty and healing to the world. Medical breakthroughs, movies that move us to tears or laughter, product innovation and technological advances that help solve the world's biggest problems – all are born of people who boldly crash status quo thinking.

Einstein believed when we're connected to creativity, there is no limit to what we can do. Our kids know this, too. They're naturally connected to their creative inner world. With no hesitation or shame, they paint yellow skies, wear costumes in public year round, and have grand visions for what they'll become when they grow up. They've yet to be conditioned by the practical, "everyone-knows-you-can't-paint-yellow-skies" mindset. Sadly, if we're not protective of their gifts, they'll learn to dismiss their inspiration and will stop dreaming.

Nurturing our boys' creativity has always been a priority to me. Playdoh, musical instruments, Legos and copious art supplies clutter our home. Writing, acting and fine art workshops have armed them with a vast array of tools to express themselves.

As much as my husband and I have enjoyed the fun, happy expressions of their creativity, we had no idea how helpful it would be when tragedy hit our family.

Three years ago, we lost my husband's dad to cancer. Two months later, my grandma died. And less than a year after that, my mom died of brain cancer – only 108 days after her terminal diagnosis. These horrific disasters were sudden, hard hitting and devastating. By the time my mom died, we'd lost six family members in less than seven years. Trauma and sadness have made regular appearances in our boys' creative work: drawings of Heaven, poems about my mom and creative writing assignments about our loved ones reflect the pain that's needed to be emptied from their hearts. The creative tools they practice open new channels to process both the ecstatic joys and gut wrenching sorrows of life.

Creativity is one of God's greatest gifts to us.
Along with developing creativity, the habit of play is essential to mental health. The other day, I asked our boys (now eleven and thirteen), "If you could talk to all the moms in the world, what would you say is the most important thing they can do for their children?" Both answered, "Play with them." Not food. Not a warm house. Not toys. It was play with them. It was a profound statement.

Play seems to be the magic superglue between a mom and her kids.
Here's the challenge to us moms: In order to play, we have to be present. And while kids are masters of the present moment, we work hard to stay one step ahead of them, tracking their constant barrage of needs. We know when they're going to be hungry again. We know who hasn't eaten veggies in three days and who hasn't pooped. We know who needs an extra hug and who needs a firm time out. And we know who needs a nap, and if we don't put them down – like right now – we'll miss that golden window and all heck will break loose. With such a mammoth database of anticipation swimming in our heads, it's tough remaining present – let alone playful.

I used to think I had to choose between being a responsible mom or a fun one: Ok, kids, I can feed you or play with you. Pick one.
But once I discovered our kids weren't asking for each day to be a Disneyland day, I was able to carve out brief activities throughout the day that were fun and doable; a few minutes of dancing in the family room, cuddling up for a read-aloud, or a session of hearty tickling. Their play tanks fill more easily than I thought.

Four years ago, our boys started training in martial arts. One day, our master instructor said to me, "You should join the adult class." And so I did.

Since then, the mat has become a playground for us. Learning new forms and weapons, performing in demonstrations and pursuing our advanced black-belt degrees together are huge bonding activities for us. As a mom, there's nothing like teaching a class and looking across the room to see our boys smiling and helping the younger belts learn curriculum. I'm present. My heart is full. And it is awesome.

Creativity and play are twin powers that help us discover and express ourselves and bond deeply with others. They help us to better express our joy, and also help us to healthfully move on after tragedy.

As moms, may we stand with Einstein and encourage our children's creativity as well as our own. And may we always make time for play.

• • • • • • • • • • • *Reflection Questions* • • • • • • • • • • •

What playful/creative things did I enjoy before having kids?

Do I still nurture my own creativity? Why not?

Is playing with my kids difficult?

How do I nurture my family's creativity?

What creative things can I do this week with my children?

Chapter Five

BOYS

· · · · · · · · · · · · · · · · · · · Lori Lara · · · · · · · · · · · · · · · · · · ·

"I have a son, who is my heart." - Maya Angelou

Many years ago, a powerful urine smell took over our downstairs bathroom. Thinking our son missed the target in his solo potty attempts, I cleaned the toilet with my homemade, non-toxic vinegar and water mixture.

The next day the odor worsened. And the next day. And the next. Despite scrubbing the toilet, floors, and walls, the stench became so appalling, I officially declared war with my bathroom. I abandoned the useless vinegar mixture and bought every toxic cleaning solution known to man. Like a mad scientist, I mixed them together, layering poison over poison, breaking all the skull-and-bones label warnings. Working in the constant flammable fog of chemicals, I eventually lost complete sense of smell. Still, the noxious reek persisted.

A week into my maddening Urine War, I walked by the open bathroom door and was completely shocked by what I saw. My son was peeing directly onto my beautiful, Pottery-Barn-cranberry, fabric shower curtain. On purpose. He'd scooted his little body two inches away and was aiming right for it.

"What are you doing?!" I gasped.

"Look, mommy!" he said with a proud smile. "The shower curtain absorbs my pee!"

The shower curtain. It was the only thing I hadn't cleaned. After a long look at what I-can't-believe-what-my-mommy-eyes-are-seeing-right-now, I composed myself as best I could, bent down, and calmly said, "Yes, it sure does absorb your pee. But, Honey, look at mommy. We don't pee on shower curtains. Ok?"

"Ok, mommy." He kissed me and hopped out of the bathroom.

Pure insanity.

As a mom of two boys, I spend an inordinate amount of time telling them what they can't do. Sometimes I can't believe what comes out of my mouth...

"No. You can't throw a rope over the second story banister and shimmy down like Batman."

"No. You can't empty our Costco-size liquid soap all over the kitchen floor to make an indoor slip-and-slide."

"No. I don't care how tough you are. You can't take turns hitting each other in the gut with a plastic bat."

"No. You can't chuck steak knives into the air to see if they'll land blade-down in the grass."

And, "No. You can't throw rocks while your brother is standing in front of you." (four stitches later, thank you very much).

Just stop it. Stop it. Stop. It. Stop all of it.

With boys, the crazy stuff happens fast. We go from fun and games to the ER in a nanosecond. A few months ago, we were at a birthday swim party less than five minutes before I heard our oldest son yelling, "Mom! Mom! He's bleeding!"

Really? I thought. I haven't even sat down.

Five stitches this time...

To my friends with daughters who color quietly or play with dolls for hours, these wild tales are pure comedy. They simply can't relate.

With all the stress of just trying to keep boys alive, one might think raising them would be pure awfulness. But nothing could be further from the truth. If you ask a boy's mom what she feels about her son, a dreamy look will wash over her face as she searches for words to describe what she feels for him. Somehow, their shenanigans melt away the moment they throw their arms around your neck and say, "I love you, Mommy." Anger and frustration are mysteriously disarmed; we are compelled by a divine bond we can't explain.

But every mom of a boy will attest that deep within that beautiful gift of indestructible love lies a great challenge.

Psychologists agree the best determiner for the kind of wife a man will seek is largely based on two factors:

1. The relationship he has with his mother and
2. How she treats his father.

I don't know about you, but that fact stops me in my tracks (especially after apologizing for "being fussy" for the umpteenth time.) Whether we realize it or not, we're establishing relational patterns our boys will crave in adulthood. If we constantly yell at them, and/or disrespect their fathers, they'll seek out women who will treat them this way. Conversely, if we allow them to be rude and walk all over us, their habitual selfishness will erode their most treasured future relationships.

For good or for heartbreak, we have the power to reach into the future, shaping the kind of husbands and fathers they'll be. *Mothering boys is serious business.* When I turn on the news and hear all the horror stories of bad male behavior, I can feel the parents of daughters begging us to do our jobs properly. Please raise your boys to love and respect our daughters.

I believe we can help redeem our truant culture by becoming mindful mothers who see beyond silly incidents with plastic bats and shower curtains. I pray we teach our boys to embrace their roles as strong leaders, willing to follow their conscience instead of the crowd. I hope we encourage that tender side of humanity living inside them, so they'll embrace the world's brokenness and be compassionate enough to ease the suffering. And I pray we establish in their hearts a longing for healthy relationships that will strengthen our families and communities.

May we confidently rise to the challenge of raising our boys, knowing that long before we chose to have children, God had a plan for us to be their moms. May we always hold tight to that special love we have for our little boys as we usher them into manhood.

· · · · · · · · · · · · · *Reflection Questions* · · · · · · · · · · · ·

What do I love most about having a son?

What are my biggest challenges?

What activities do my son and I both enjoy? Make a list together.

What areas do I need to improve?

What can I do today to show my son how much I love him?

Chapter Six

WORDS

• • • • • • • • • • • • • • • • • • Mandy Arioto • • • • • • • • • • • • • • • • • •

"Think twice before you speak, because your words and influence will plant the seed of either success or failure in the mind of another." – Napoleon Hill

The women in my family are approachable. I am told we have picked up this trait from the generations before us who have bequeathed it to us. It is a personal quality that makes people feel uncommonly comfortable telling us whatever they are thinking. In my case, not only do they feel comfortable spilling their own secrets, they also feel free to tell me things about myself that may be rude or inappropriate in normal conversation. I secretly like it. It is so fascinating to get a glimpse into other people's lives that I can usually enjoy whatever they may have put out there into the universe of words. Plus it always makes for a good story.

I have had an OBGYN comment on the lack of tissue I have in my breasts (read that as small boobs), I have had a man in an oil change shop share with me how he only had two months to live and engaged me in a sacred conversation about his biggest regrets in life, and my kids continue to remind me that I have THE WORST breath in the morning and to never breathe on them before I have brushed my teeth. So precious.

A few months ago I stood up in front of a bunch of women and shared a few pictures and talked about random things that I had been thinking about. At the end of the presentation, the ladies who I shared an hour spilling my heart to filled out a comment card about my talk. There was a line for things they appreciated and another line for additional comments. As I lay in bed in my hotel room that night reading through lots of comment cards, one particular card locked eyes with me and engaged in an epic staring contest. I couldn't take my eyes off of it. It said, "Mandy's outfit screams: I'm fancy, too cool, unrelatable, and I get to shop all the time." I remember it verbatim – because I kept it. I threw away every other comment card – the ones with kind words – and stashed this one with the daggers to look at later.

Here is the behind the scenes truth about my outfit: (and p.s. I feel a little crazy even talking about this – but sometimes we have to be truth-tellers and that means feeling a little off center.) So, the truth about my outfit... I hadn't gone shopping in at least five months. I sat on the bed the night before I left for this particular talk and shed tears to my husband because I had nothing to wear. So I wore five-year-old jeans and boots and a bomber jacket that I have had since college that has pleather cracking and falling off at the elbows.

I know that this may sound silly, but that comment hurt. In some weird way it nullified the stories I shared about my life and the weeks I took preparing to stand before this group of women and share vulnerable pieces of myself. All because someone who was sitting in the room felt like the jeans I was wearing made me unrelatable.

Thankfully my mom was with me on this particular trip, and was able to talk me out of the pity party I felt like throwing myself. Even weeks later, I can't help but wonder at the power of words both – written and verbalized – to leave indentations on our soul that can shape us for life.

I grew up in a house where words were lavish. My brother and I had two parents who helped us believe that we were valuable. They poured out praise and affection that convinced us our artistic prowess at finger painting would have made Monet jealous. According to mom and dad, our athletic talent was more entertaining to watch than anything on ESPN, and the way we crafted conversation rivaled the script of a feature film. There were a lot of things that we didn't have growing up. We didn't have a VCR until I was in high school. We didn't shop at Express. My first car was a ten year old Nissan Sentra that didn't shift into 5th gear, purchased with tip money from waitressing all through high school. Do you know how often any of that mattered? Never. What we did have were parents who we knew loved us with words that made us feel valuable. With so many words.

Some people worry that if we speak words of affirmation over our kids that they will begin to think that the world revolves around them. I couldn't disagree more. As far as I can tell the world offers all of us a plethora of opportunities to be humiliated, put in our place and criticized for our flaws. That is why I believe my job or rather my privilege as a mom is to speak words over my kids that will remind them day after day that they are valuable.

My task is to tell my children they are beautiful and wanted, and full of gifts that the world needs. It is the words we use that will heal our kids wounded places. Similar words that God took great care to speak over us, reminding us that even in our pain we are valuable. It is not coming unglued over spilled drinks and lost shoes, injuring their little spirits in the process with words that will define them. Our task is to utter thousands of ordinary sentences filled with millions of loving words to our children while they live under our roofs; to measure our words carefully, because they carry weight to shape the future.

Here is the truth, sisters: Our. Words. Are. Powerful.

There is this crazy part in the beginning of God's story in the world where God gives humanity the ability to name all of the animals, essentially to give them an identity. From that point forward God has gifted all of humanity with the same gift. To speak over one another who we are and who we are becoming.

The words that we use have tremendous power to bless and to curse.

I am not suggesting that we shouldn't be honest or vulnerable about how we are really feeling. What I am saying is that we can't let the words we speak over the world to be influenced by our own uncomfortable feelings. So the next time I meet someone whose jeans make me feel like they may be unrelatable (what does that even mean?), I am going to walk right over to her and ask if anything funny happened to her yet that morning. Or when one of my kids spills a bowl of milk I'll tell them about the time when I was a waitress and spilled a whole cup of red Hawaiian punch on a lady wearing a white blouse, and remind myself that nothing is so precious we should sacrifice healing words on the altar of spilled milk.

It takes a year to learn how to talk – and a lifetime to learn what to say. So I am choosing to spend my lifetime telling people what I see in them. Pointing them toward the beautiful parts of who they are and who they are becoming. I want to be someone who offers redemption to the ones who have been wounded by words. Because words are art & medicine. They possess potent healing power.

And my children will never want for words of blessing. I will speak over them lavishly and extravagantly because sometimes we have to tell people who they are before they can become it. It is when we speak over someone that something comes to life in their souls and they can start believing that it is true.

Chapter Seven

VULNERABILITY

• •Lori Lara• • • • • • • • • • • • • • • • • • • •

"If we want to live and love with our whole hearts, and if we want to engage with the world from a place of worthiness, we have to talk about the things that get in the way—especially shame, fear, and vulnerability." — Brené Brown

I love the way my good friend Anamaria views rejection.

She says, "I don't have time to worry about people not liking me. If someone isn't going to like me, then fine; I want to know as quickly as possible so I can get on to finding the people who will."

What a fantastic concept, right? Instead of running away from rejection, she runs straight through it. She's unwilling to alter herself for the sake of being liked.

From a young age, I spent most of my time avoiding rejection. I became a chameleon, censoring what I said to match what I thought people wanted to hear, shading my opinions to align with others, and being quiet when I didn't agree.

My mantra was: Blend in, don't be weak, and then you won't get hurt. Fear took away my voice and vulnerability.

I dragged this self-protection straight into adulthood. One day a friend confronted my invulnerability during a very uncomfortable conversation in front of some other friends.

Here's what happened:

I had hurt my back, so my friend offered to cook dinner for my family.

"Oh, no. Thanks, but you don't have to do that," I said.

"I know I don't have to. I want to."

"No, really. I can handle it." Smiling, I thought this would end the exchange.

It didn't.

"I really want to cook dinner for you."

"You're really sweet. Thanks, but I've got it."

At this point, the conversation felt silly. We were in a tug-of-war over who was going to cook my dinner.

Her face turned serious. Our friends watched silently.

"Lori, remember when you cooked dinner for me a few weeks ago? And then you took me to the doctor last week and fed my dogs when I was out of town?

"Yes, I remember."

"Ok, how did you feel when you did those things for me?"

I had no clue where she was taking this banter, but I either wanted to crack a joke to lighten the mood or I wanted to run – anything to get away from the uneasy feeling in my chest.

"I was happy to help you."

"Ok, when you don't let me help you, you're robbing me of the joy of giving to you."

You're robbing me of the joy of giving to you.

Wow. I'd never thought about it like that.

She really got me thinking. Why don't I let my friends help me, even though I love helping them?

The answer was this: in order to accept help, I had to be vulnerable. And vulnerability scared me to death.

Maybe you can relate?

Motherhood brings our fear of vulnerability to an epic level, doesn't it? Lord, have mercy. Nothing says I'm totally not in control like chasing a screaming, naked toddler around the park who insists on peeing on the slide. In a series of embarrassing moments, our precious, uncivilized munchkins rip our chameleon masks right off our faces, exposing us to the stares and glares of others. Exposing us to rejection.

My first big mommy mortification happened during our son's preschool Christmas musical at church. The packed audience let out a collective "Awwww" as the line of adorable, shy preschoolers made their way on stage. Out of nowhere my son busted out of line and acted out the most audacious rock star air guitar performance you've ever seen. The audience burst into laughter, and I desperately searched for that hole in the earth we pray for when things like this happen. The laughter was gasoline to his theatrical fire. He kept doing it. I found myself looking at the crowd as they were laughing and looking back at me, and all I could do was shrug my shoulders in disbelief while I mouthed the words, I don't know where he learned this. I swear we don't watch MTV.

As moms, we either settle our fear of vulnerability, or we spend the rest of our mothering journey exhausted and stressed over trying to stuff our kids into a blender, trying to pour them into molds they weren't made to fit.

For me, the work of becoming vulnerable began about eight years ago. In professional counseling, I traced the roots of my insecurity to damaging childhood experiences that caused me to not only shut out people – but to shut out God. As part of my spiritual healing, I pursued God with all my heart. During a time of intense prayer and meditation, I entered into vulnerable space with God, revealing all my hurts. With nothing to offer but brokenness, instead of feeling rejection, I felt the tenderest love filling me. It was warm and safe, and like nothing I'd ever experienced.

You don't have to hide from Me; I know you and I love you.

The spiritual intimacy moved me so profoundly I cried on and off for weeks. The sense of belonging and acceptance broke old patterns of self-protection and freed me to find my voice again.

Intimacy is that magical place of being known and knowing someone else. It doesn't mean sharing our entire life stories with everyone we meet; it means being real, and peeling back our outer layers to experience true closeness. This kind of holy confidence is a legit super power that grows stronger as we practice it. As moms, when we stand confidently in the freedom of who we are, we can pass on a powerful mantra to our kids: Don't blend in, do life deeply with others – then you'll experience one of the greatest joys in life: Intimacy.

• • • • • • • • • • • • • *Reflection Questions* • • • • • • • • • • • •

Do I have difficulty asking for help?

Growing up, how was vulnerability modeled to me?

What does intimacy mean to me?

How can I become more vulnerable with my loved ones?

How can I help my children learn vulnerability?

Chapter Eight

FRIENDSHIP

• • • • • • • • • • • • • • • • • • Lori Lara • • • • • • • • • • • • • • • • • • •

Friendship is born at the moment when one person says to another, "What! You, too? I thought I was the only one." – C.S. Lewis

Has a close friend ever broken your heart? I mean, really, really broken it. The kind of broken where you decide you'll never trust another friend as long as you live?

I have. Twice.

My first year in college, I found out one of my closest friends was dating my boyfriend behind my back – for an entire month – before she finally confessed. "I'm in love with him," she said.

I didn't see this truck coming. My brain couldn't process the news. All I could think about was all the time we spent together, and how much I'd trusted this girl.

"It's ok. We'll work it out." I stepped closer and put my hands on her arms to comfort her. To comfort her.

Oh, my stomach hurts remembering my naiveté and vulnerability in that moment.

My friend went on to explain that she wasn't going to end the relationship, because remember – she was "in love with him."

Big ouch.

This was my initiation into the heart-ripping world of friend betrayal. If you're like a lot of women I know, you've experienced this kind of hurt, too. Betrayal is uniquely awful, isn't it?

The second time my friend heart was broken, it was more tragic. My best childhood friend Shannon was killed by a drunk driver. We grew up together on the same street from the time we were two years old, and our closeness was unmatched by any other friendship. She loved our boys like her own, and they adored her. She was truly my sister.

When I lost Shannon, I was in the middle of a serious breakdown and newly in recovery from major depression and PTSD. When I got the phone call she was gone, I walked around in a numb haze for a long, long time. Helping our boys process their grief while dealing with my own was brutal; the only thing worse than crying your guts out is watching your kids do it. Thank God I was already in intensive therapy at the time. I'm not sure I would have made it out of that dark place without the help of my counselor.

After Shannon died, I put a CLOSED sign over my heart; no friend would ever get that close to me again. I focused all my energy on my family and newfound recovery, and I sincerely believed I'd be ok spending the rest of my life with superficial friends.

I was wrong.

As a new mom, I often felt isolated and lonely. I loved our kids, but I was fighting through recovery while managing the daily mayhem of crushed cheerios, exhaustion, and 3-day-old dirty hair. I needed friends to tell me the struggle was normal, and that life would open up as I grew into motherhood. I needed another perspective on my life – one I couldn't see through the tears.

Knowing my painful history, my husband suggested I ask God to bring trustworthy friends into my life. At first I felt silly praying for friends. With wars and world hunger, wanting friends seemed trivial, and not exactly prayer-worthy. Despite my doubt, I began praying for friends.

To my surprise, I quickly met some great women at church, including another new mom named Amy. I had an immediate feeling Amy and I were supposed to be friends, so one rainy day after passing each other in the school corridor, I turned around and said, "Um… I think we are supposed to be friends. Do you want to have coffee sometime?"

Awkward, right?

We still laugh about it, but that day was the start to an incredibly open, vulnerable, and safe friendship; a friendship I was sure I'd never have again.
In the years following that first prayer for friendship, I've been blessed with an amazing posse of friends. Two years ago, my world was shattered again

when my mom was diagnosed with terminal brain cancer. She died just 108 days after diagnosis. While my family and I were burying my mom, my angel friends worked together to set up a beautiful reception in our home. With fresh cemetery mud on my shoes, I walked into my house with my family. It was filled with food and drinks, accented with flowers, candles and heart-felt cards. They brought beauty into my darkness. All I could do was weep over their generous love.

For an entire month, friends from my martial arts school and homeschooling community delivered meals so I could grieve with my family without having to think about cooking. Every other night I was greeted with hot food and open arms that let me just cry.

Whether we're laughing at our crazy mommy stories or multi-tasking serious phone calls while cooking dinner, the message my friends offer is clear:

I'm here. I care. I'll walk this journey with you – no matter what.

Friendship is vital to a healthy life. And as moms, we get to show our kids what it means to share life closely with others. They have front row seats to the balance of giving and receiving, and what it means to be there in good and hard times.

These days, my heart is OPEN to friendship. If you have close friends who love you and feed your spirit, I encourage you to continue nurturing those relationships. If you've been hurt by a friend, and you're feeling isolated and in need of friendship, I'm praying today will be the beginning of your healing.

· · · · · · · · · · · · · *Reflection Questions* · · · · · · · · · · · · ·

What do I value most in friendship? (i.e. holding a confidence, open communication, vulnerability, not gossiping)?

What painful experiences have affected my ability to trust other women?

How do my friends help me see my life differently?

What are some things I can do this week to show my friends how much I care about them?

How can I help my children foster healthy friendships?

Chapter Nine

STRESS

· Lori Lara ·

"When my kids become wild and unruly, I use a nice, safe playpen. When they're finished, I climb out." — Erma Bombeck

When I was pregnant with our first son, I watched a fascinating television interview between an American journalist who was pregnant with her first child and a mother living in a rural village in Africa. My interest piqued as I, too, was immersed in my own baby education. The mother-to-be reporter asked the veteran mother what she should expect when her first baby was born. I'll never forget what the African mom said.

With no hesitation, she said, "You will need to be a warrior."

Whoa. A warrior?
It was the strangest comment I'd ever heard about becoming a mom. I'd never read anything in my baby books about becoming a warrior. I thought with a bit of research, motherhood would come naturally.

Maybe it's harder for her because she doesn't have any modern conveniences, I thought.

But those beautiful dark eyes reached through the TV and told me there was something she knew. Something I'd soon learn.

My warrior training started immediately after our first son was born. All at once, I was filled with love, but I was quickly buried by the enormous work of caring for him. After a year of debilitating sleep deprivation, I informed my husband that our beloved son would have to be an only child. I was crying and felt tremendous guilt, but I just couldn't take care of another baby.

The next day I found out I was pregnant.

Growing up fiercely independent, I believed I should handle motherhood on my own. Life had to grind this self-reliance out of me, one painful experience at a time.

This was one of those crushing times:

It was the end of a hectic day. Our boys were toddler age and I was frazzled and exhausted. I sat with my husband at the kitchen table as he ate his late dinner. My Mother-in-Law was playing with the boys in the family room just a few feet away from us.

I was done. Done. Mommy done.

I should have just said goodnight and let my husband take care of the evening routine. But I didn't. As he ate and we talked, he started doing something that bothered me. I don't remember what it was that annoyed me, probably just joking around. Whatever it was, I wasn't in the mood. It got under my skin, clashing with my rattled nerves that were screaming for me to get out of the kitchen. I felt this massive monster of stress growing in my stomach as he continued to do that pestering thing I can't remember. Finally, I warned him if he did it again, I'd do something about it. We were in that space of we're kind of kidding, but I'm totally not kidding.

He called my bluff doing his joking thing again and I cracked wide open and did what any mature woman would do. I threw my entire glass of water on him—right in front of his mother. I seriously lost it. I was so far over the mommy cliff you'd need a search and rescue crew to hoist me back. Instantly mortified by what I'd done, I tried pretending I was joking. But there was just no playing off the fact that both he and his dinner plate were dripping with water.

Having no emotional bandwidth to jump the chasm back to sanity, I ran out of the house in a full-tilt bawl and drove away in my car. I was embarrassed and didn't know how to make it right.

I can't believe I just did that! What is happening to me?

Two minutes later my cell phone rang. It was my husband.

The conversation went something like this:

"I'm falling apart! I haven't eaten a proper meal or washed my hair in 3 days. My entire day is spent decoding mysterious cries and missed naps. You have no idea how hard it is taking care of our kids all the time. Try peeing in a public bathroom while holding one child in your arms and watching helplessly while the other one combat crawls on the feces-infested floor shamelessly peeking at the lady in the next stall asking if she has to poop. Look, I love you, but I'm chronically dirty with no hope for a shower because I can't leave them alone for a single second. I'm exhausted and barely a woman anymore. I just can't do this anymore!"

At which point only the dogs in the neighborhood could hear my high-squeal rant.

I loved our children more than anything, but somewhere along the mommyhood path, my needs had completely fallen off the table. Deep resentment rooted in my heart, and *I needed help learning how to care for myself while balancing the needs of my family.* Thankfully, after years of struggling alone, I got the professional help I needed.

My only regret is that I didn't reach out sooner. I suffered needlessly for too long.

Motherhood is a much easier adjustment once we realize we're not alone in the battle. Any mom worth her weight in experience will admit making peace with domestic chaos wasn't immediate. It was a process. Knowing other moms feel that awful isolation keeps me up at night. And that's exactly why I write so openly about my early struggles and recovery. The truth is we're never alone.

Even though we might live continents away from each other, we're deeply connected in the tribe of motherhood – working side by side, sharing hard earned wisdom and encouragement, and doing our best to become the warriors one beautiful African mother said we'd be.

· · · · · · · · · · · · *Reflection Questions* · · · · · · · · · · ·

What am I most anxious about?

Where do I go when I'm stressed?

What aspect of parenting do I need the most help with?

What can I do this week to help myself?

How can I support the other moms in my life?

Chapter Ten

SORROW

• • • • • • • • • • • • • • • Mandy Arioto • • • • • • • • • • • • • •

"My ambition was to live like music." — Mary Gaitskill

I must be PMSing. That or I'm going through some kind of thirty-life crisis. Or maybe it is the fact that the dog ate my favorite pair of boots.

Those are the only reasons I can think of for this morning's breakdown on the way to school drop-off. An old Counting Crows song came on and suddenly it was fifteen years ago, and I was on a train somewhere between San Louis Obispo and San Diego, headphones on, sitting next to Drea and choking back tears over a boy who wasn't good for me anyway.

In the now it's a thousand Wednesdays from that day, and I'm listening to the Counting Crows sing over the speakers in my car while two little girls who look just like me sit in the back seat. And I remember exactly how it felt to be on that train and can't help but feel like everything is different now, but really nothing much has changed. I am the same girl who cries at songs, just without the train or the scrunchies at the bottom of my purse. Not that I even carry a purse anymore. Purses are too small for today's life. Just like some songs are too big.

Music has the capacity to hold deep delight; it can also make sorrow sound beautiful. And I wonder what it means to live – like music. To be ok with all the feelings, and to create out of them all something worth sharing.

When we hear lyrics that remind us of a moment, what if we paused to feel them?

When the deep pangs of sorrow wash over you, when you can smell the basement of your Grandma's house or remember the moment you saw blood and realized the pregnancy was over, or when pangs of embarrassment about losing that job sweep through your gut, or you realize marriage is lonelier than you thought it was going to be. Those are the moments to pause and consider: dark feelings come occasionally – and maybe that is ok.

Has anyone ever told you that it is ok to be in a dark place? Instead of trying to outrun the pain, try sitting with it for a while. Look it in the eye, and acknowledge that it is there. Is it possible that your pain, whatever it may be, is simply waiting to be seen and acknowledged before it can pass?

What if we redeemed sorrow? If we called it good and recognized that sorrow is part of our humanity – a delicate melody that weaves humanity with the holy and allows us to empathize with the hurting places in the world and in our own hearts.

My friend Glennon Melton at momastery.com talks about how she lives a valley life. (Watch her video in your MOPS group. You're welcome. This girl is wise.) She says that life is lived fuller in the valleys. That everybody thinks the mountaintops are the place to be, but up there the air's so thin you can barely breathe and there's nothing to do but stare at the view. Down in the valley is where the water runs. In the valley is where all the power is. In fact Glennon says that everything she likes about life happens in the valley. Because it is in the valley where we learn and feel and transform and see glimmers of God. These things happen in the valley – not on the mountaintops.

Glennon says she has learned three ways to help her navigate sorrow. Here is my take on her idea:

Take Care of Yourself
Often it feels indulgent or selfish to care for ourselves. How can we find the time to care for our body and soul when all the other bodies around us have such pressing needs? It seems to me that somewhere along the journey we women have decided that it is okay to run ourselves ragged as long as everyone around us is taken care of. Maybe it is time to call a truce. To sit for a minute and listen to what your body is saying. And just like we rush to care for a crying baby or a hungry toddler, what if we extend that same care to ourselves? Are there places where your body is hurting? Is your soul parched? Is there something you know deep in your gut you need to do to care for yourself? Take a few minutes to come home to yourself and remember that your body and soul need the same care you extend to the people you love most.

Identify as a Soul – Not a Role
When we are young we know what we love and what we love to do. We

don't measure our value by what we have or what our titles are. Instead we are simply us. As we grow and become full-fledged adults, our hearts change a little. Suddenly the first question that we ask one another is, "What do you do?" Wouldn't it be interesting if instead we posed a question that told us more about one another, "What do you love?" Perhaps it is time to reclaim our birthright. To remember what we love, and what fills our soul with delight. May we take the time to remember and to be able to answer these questions well: What do you love? What fills your soul? What do you find beautiful, and how can you immerse yourself in splendor?

Go ahead and BE Brokenhearted
Too often we spend our time trying to outrun pain, to be one step ahead, to stay so busy that we don't ever have to admit to what our insides are feeling. That's why we drink and eat and cheat and shop and hit and gossip and hurt each other. Because we cannot handle our difficult feelings. Because we cannot trust pain as a teacher. We are like caterpillars who constantly quit right before we emerge as butterflies. What if we stopped running from pain and decided to be still and to trust the process?

And when our kids get their feelings hurt or feel sad about breaking a toy, perhaps we just learn to sit with them in their sorrow instead of rushing in to distract them from their feelings or replace their broken toy. Could it be that the best way to show up for others who are deep in sorrow is to simply sit and share in their sorrow? Without offering words that act as pathetic bandaids clinging to gaping wounds, perhaps we simply sit and breathe alongside them, allowing our presence to be enough.

Build Altars
Ok, I am going to add one last thought to Glennon's list. When sorrow is near, it helps to look to the good. The good is found in altars that we build during the daylight, when things didn't look so dark. There is a saying: Forgetfulness leads to exile; Remembrance leads to redemption. When life is good, take the time to build altars. Journal, celebrate, feast. Create markers that you can look to, to be reminded of the inherent goodness of living. This will look different for each of us. I have a wall in my house where I hang a random assortment of photos of Joe and I when we first met, a cross-stitch picture of my horse from when I was ten, art my kids have made, a postcard my friend Drea mailed me from her honeymoon and a blessing my mom wrote for me. This wall is my reminder, an altar of sorts, to celebrate the goodness that surrounds me. My wall is a powerful visual reminder of goodness for the times I struggle to find the good.

Look to the good and be reminded that God is with us in both the daylight and darkness.

May we decide to feel deeply. May we realize that each of us can choose to tell our story a thousand different ways. The very definition of flourishing is to choose, instead of "tragedy," to call the moments in our lives what they really are: Epic. What you see in front of you may be far outside of what you dreamed, but when you have the boldness to call it beautiful instead of calling it cursed, you are taking part in something holy.

May we sit with sorrow and build altars of delight, reminding ourselves that even though we have wounds – we are still called to sing.

• • • • • • • • • • • • *Reflection Questions* • • • • • • • • • • • •

When have you lived like music?

If you chose a song to represent your life, what would it be?

What do you love – what makes your heart sing?

Name a moment in your life that felt tragic. Now reframe it – how did you learn and grow through this event or series of events? How did it make you who you are? How did it shape you?

What can you do this week to build an altar of goodness?

Chapter Eleven

MARRIAGE

Emily T. Wierenga

"Don't marry the person you think you can live with; marry only the individual you think you can't live without."
- James Dobson

The other night we left the boys with my sister and rented a hotel room in the mountains. We planned to snowboard the next day.

We bought some beer and take-out and I couldn't rest that night. For hours, we lay there in our separate beds because the room came with two, but I couldn't sleep. And I cried.

Trent stretched out his hand across the space between our beds, his fingers reaching for me in the dark. "Hold on to me, Em," he said. "I'm here."

We're not exactly John and Yoko.

Trent's a math geek and I'm a literary nerd. He's loud and I'm quiet. He's athletic and I run into walls. We both like books. We both love camping. And we're both over-the-moon crazy about each other and our boys.

But marriage has come hard for us.

Hard, with years of anorexia and insomnia and fists punching the wall.

A few weeks after our snowboarding trip, I was putting away laundry, the seven loads which Trent folded for me while playing a computer game, because between my books and my boys, I can't seem to take a shower or do any house cleaning –let alone fold the laundry.

And I was putting the baskets away when he called "Suppertime," because Trent's made burgers, and on the table, a salad: with peppers and Jalapeno cheese, lettuce, bacon bits, and grated carrot, and chopped onions which always make Trent cry–it's the only time I see him cry – and "I made you fancy salad," he said.

There's nothing sexier than a salad-making man.

And the truth is, I'd be a wreck without him.

The one who held me those long, skinny anorexia years.

Our best conversations happen over a board game because games are Trent's love language, and we're still getting the intimacy thing.

I used to fight him when I got mad, sometimes with my fists, and he'd shake his head and grab my wrists and then finally leave. Slam the door and drive off while I wept into the couch pillows, but that doesn't happen anymore.

No man is perfect, and Trent will say things that unintentionally hurt me, or he'll forget to take out the trash, but I will also do things – like forget his birthday, as I did one year – and ours is the kind of marriage that throbs with love.

The kind of love that will not give up: not through anorexia, not through insomnia, not through moves to Korea or moves home to take care of parents with cancer, not through slammed doors or tears or fists – because there's also the salad. There's the laundry. There's Trent taking the kids to his parents so I can write. There's him reaching out in the dark to hold me, to pray for me.

I want the kind of marriage that dances into its Golden Anniversary; that kisses each other on wrinkled cheeks and laughs at each other's jokes long after the sun has wound down.

And maybe the secret is to never stop reaching out in the dark. To never stop taking hold of each other's hands. And to never let go.

Not even for a moment.

Has your marriage ever suffered a rough patch? How have you gotten through it?

How are you and your husband different? Similar? How does not focusing on those traits but rather, just on the love you share, help to forgive the misunderstandings?

Why is it so hard for us as women to believe we are not only loved, but lovable? What can we do to change this?

How has having children affected your marriage/date nights? What can you do to revive date nights if they've gone stagnant?

What can you do this week to revive romance in the midst of daily life?

Chapter Twelve

RHYTHMS

• • • • • • • • • • • • • • • • • Mandy Arioto • • • • • • • • • • • • • • • •

"Life is about rhythm. We vibrate, our hearts are pumping blood, we are a rhythm machine, that's what we are."
- Mickey Hart

It's a lovely Friday morning, and I'm home, happily in my pajamas. The house is quiet, I am ignoring the dishes in the sink and allowing myself be slow and a little flaky this morning. This is not my normal hectic morning routine, and I am reveling in the change of rhythm. Sometimes I don't realize what a hectic pace I run at until I linger in my jammies for a morning and the house is so quiet that I can actually hear my own heart beating.

The world as we know it beats to a rhythm. The sun rises and sets every day, the seasons change four times a year and our bodies ebb and flow to a lunar cycle. We live by an inhale, exhale, inhale, exhale rhythm, but we rarely stop to notice it.

Finding rhythm and balance in our lives is essential for resetting our inner compass and connecting with our inner wisdom. When we don't rest, we lose our way. When we don't rest, the people in our lives become an object of our ambition, and a line item in a growing list of obligations. When we don't rest we are telling ourselves that the entire world is on our shoulders, and if we STOP. Life will come crashing down. That's a lot of unspoken pressure to bear.

Sometimes we need a break from the churning of life's priorities to find the rhythm that suits our soul – the heartbeat that lets us take care of business while embracing life to the full.

I get to talk with a lot of women over the course of a year, and almost always they will share with me about their lives. (That is something I love about women, we are really good at confiding in one another.) There are two things that almost every woman tells me. The first is that they are exhausted and the second is that they feel like they aren't doing enough with their lives.

Exhausted because they are doing so much – and also terrified that they aren't doing enough. Um…

Girls — we need to talk about this.

These are women who live all over the country with the same nagging feelings. And it isn't just women I meet; it is my friends who I know best. My friend Kristen stays at home with her four kids and only sleeps four hours a night so that she can run an Etsy shop from her house, Lacey is running a Crossfit gym with her husband and just had a new baby, Alicia is staying home and raising the two most enchanting children I've ever met while also trying to launch a photography business. Mikkee works a full time job in four days a week and then – because she doesn't have any kids of her own, has chosen to move in with her best friend Stephanie in order to help Stephanie and her husband raise their kids and in her "spare time" takes on as many freelance writing projects as possible. Leilani volunteers at her kid's preschool so often that one of the other parents thought she was a paid teacher.

From all appearances one would assume that each of my friends would be filled with feelings of accomplishment, but instead they swirl with constant doubt, worrying that they are failing at life. Alicia worries that she's wasting her education by staying home with her kids. Kristen worries that she's endangering her marriage by working such long hours. Lacey is already worrying that she is screwing up her kid and he is only three months old, and Mikkee is worried that she is so busy she will never meet someone she wants to spend the rest of her life with.

And all of them worry that they won't be able to fit into their skinny jeans.

The thing is, it hurts my guts to talk to so many women who feel like they aren't thriving. And then a few days ago I was talking to a friend of mine who not so diplomatically reminded me that I am feeling the same things. Like how I can't sleep through the night because I wake up worrying about all of the things in my life that seem to need worrying about, or how I have needed to start saying no to commitments for a really long time – but haven't because I feel guilty that I will let people down.

It feels to me like we, as a generation of sisters who are raising the world together, might need to call a time out. To call everyone in for a huddle and maybe find more life giving ways to move through the world. Because there are too many of us who are waking up at 3 o'clock in the morning and abusing ourselves for everything we aren't. Aren't doing, aren't being, aren't getting right.

We are so busy that we are losing the ability to be human. To live by a human pace, to have lingering conversations with pregnant pauses where no one feels rushed to fill the silence, the ability to smell the orange blossoms blooming in the spring.

It seems to me that we need less striving and more life.

I think we should start a conversation that we can take to the playgrounds and Gymboree and all the places we moms hang out, where we can call a truce with our striving. Then we can all pinky swear that we will think about dropping the crazy-making expectations that we are putting on ourselves. Expectations that we must be perfect mothers and perfect lovers with perfect bodies who run charities that are changing the world while we do the hardest yoga poses and post them on Instagram.

We are forging our own paths, and because of that we need to show ourselves and one another some compassion.

So if this is you –

If you crave deeper friendships but the time or energy for them.

If you feel like you haven't taken a deep breath in years.

If you are exhausted and craving rest.

If you feel depleted by giving so much to the world around you that you have forgotten how to care for yourself.

I have a gut feeling that our collective solution is found in a really weird word called Sabbath, coupled with becoming religious – about play.

Sabbath is a concept that comes from our Jewish friends. They recognize that God has instructed us to rest, and they take that very seriously. So they take a full 24 hours where they focus on rest and slowing down. Not only that, but if you were to go to Israel for Sabbath you would find that at the end of the 24 hours of rest, they celebrate like it is Christmas and

Easter all wrapped into one. They celebrate like this every single week.

Or in other words, they rest and play.

I come from a faith tradition that admires people who can sit still and quiet for a long time. I love spending time by myself in quiet, but the truth is it usually isn't good for me. It turns out I am better around people who can remind me who I am. I was talking with a good friend of mine named Jared about this, and he shared with me about a conversation he had with a spiritual director. He was telling his spiritual director about how he had decided to incorporate more silence and solitude into his life. But his spiritual director looked at him while he was talking and said, "Well, why would you do that?" Jared's reply was, "because it's really good for me and I need to figure some things out." But the response of his director surprised him, "Why don't you do the things that are really life giving to you? Like, go have a meal with good people and paint pictures and just enjoy life. Play." Jared shared with me that it was an interesting reorienting of what he needed to hear at that point.

I think sometimes we need to hear, "Be still and quiet." And sometimes we need to hear, "Go play and spend time with people." When we reorient ourselves to the fact that rest isn't just silence and solitude, but rather anything that gives us life, it makes the concept of slowing down so much more enjoyable.

A few thoughts that might spark some ideas on how to rest and play:

- Start doing things you love to do. An acquaintance asked me a little while ago about what hobbies I have… I had no answers. So I started thinking about what kind of hobbies would I like to have? Then I thought back to the things I was drawn to as a kid, because I believe that some of our birthright gifts are evident even as kids. Now I know this sounds ridiculous to some of you who have really littles at home and are so exhausted that you can barely make yourself a cup of coffee in the morning. To you I say: Your hobby is sleep. There will be time for other life giving activities later.

- One thing we do is to make a list of "play day" activities to do as a family every month. We usually come up with a handful of ideas, and then on the days we have set aside for play we refer to our list. This helps eliminate the "what should we do?" conversation. This particular month we want to go horseback riding, eat cannolis, build a snow igloo and take our dogs for a long hike.

- This one might hurt a little... *Maybe we need to recalibrate our understanding of rest.*

You guys, we are on our devices. All. The. Freaking. Time. The problem is that rest isn't binge watching tv, it isn't checking out for hours on end. Distractions are different than rest. I can spend an hour looking at buzzfeed on my phone, but that doesn't give me life. It distracts me from life. Rest is participating in things that are rejuvenating. Make a list of the distractions you choose and analyze whether they are contributing to your own soul care – or just delaying it.

- Sometimes we need a break in a beautiful place to figure everything out. The voice of nature is what I prefer. When is the last time you walked around barefoot? Or grabbed a blanket and lay out under the stars. Maybe nature is where you will get in touch with the rhythms of the universe. Get outside and walk in the mud.

- Forget about the laundry. Seriously. It is never going to be finished. That is the truth. Let it pile up for a day. It will be waiting for you after you have rested.

One last thing. When you start to choose rest and play, you may experience all the feelings. All. Of. The. Feelings.

You might need to address the fact that rest feels indulgent. Or the feelings of shame that come when we don't feel productive. Or sometimes uncomfortable emotions surface when we get quiet. Emotions that have been drowned out by background noise of busyness come to the surface when we slow down. My own demons of not being able to say no (because I am such a people pleaser) get exercised when I practice rest. With each no our shame may increase, because when we stop, the world starts rushing past us – making us feel like we are left behind, like we are losing, like we are missing something. But what we are missing is the adrenaline rush of busy. *And busy isn't a pace we can keep forever.*

Sabbath keeping requires relaxing into the humble, small human rhythms of rest and play. To practice Sabbath means to go quiet, to be less noticed, to stop striving and rest in the ordinary.

It takes courage to rest and play but our souls need it like our bodies need oxygen.

So to all my sisters who feel exhausted, may this be a season where you experience less and more. Less hustling. Less proving. Less frantic. Less bone-tired. More play. More connection. More life, more prayer, more sacred space.

May your hearts hear a new rhythm that compels you toward deeper breaths and feasts of laughter. And may this coming season of your life be filled with profound nourishment as you change the rhythms of your world by resting and playing.

• • • • • • • • • • • • • *Reflection Questions* • • • • • • • • • • • •

What things in your life are you using as mechanisms for rest (Pinterest, Facebook, 90's era sitcom reruns), but may just be distractions?

What activity(s) could you stop to allow more time in your schedule for rest or play?

On an average day, do you feel rested? Do you allow your family the space they need to feel rested?

When is the last time you played? Not Legos or Candyland or Hide-and-Seek – when is the last time you played at something that renews your spirit, just for you?

What chore bogs you down most? Is it laundry, dishes, meal planning or something else? What can you do this week to delegate some of your workload to another source (paid laundry service once in awhile, for instance) or relax your standards on (buy a few more cereal bowls so you can fuss with dishes a little less often).

Chapter Thirteen

SEEING PEOPLE DIFFERENTLY

• • • • • • • • • • • • • • Emily T. Wierenga • • • • • • • • • • • • • •

"You are the one that decides what defines you."
– Lizzie Velasquez

It's Saturday. I'm scrolling through the newsfeed on Facebook when I discover a TED Talk featuring "The Ugliest Woman in the World" and how she's found happiness.

Lizzie Velasquez was born without amniotic fluid cushioning her. Doctors could not believe she was alive, but she came out screaming and didn't know until kindergarten that there was anything different about her.

She didn't know until she walked up to a little girl and smiled, and the girl looked as though she'd seen a monster. That's when Lizzie [www. aboutlizzie.com] found out she had a syndrome which, among other challenges, prevented her from ever gaining weight and from seeing out of one eye.

When she was a teenager, Lizzie stumbled upon a video labeling her the Ugliest Woman in the World; a video which showed silent footage of her and had been viewed by millions and commented on by thousands, some of whom told her to do the world a favor and put a gun to her head.

This is the world we live in. A world which mutes a person's voice and YouTubes their body.

Lizzie cried when she read those words, and she wanted to fight back. Instead, *she decided to take those negative comments and use them as rungs on a ladder to get where she wanted to go.*

She determined to fight fear with dreams. To become a motivational speaker, to write a book, to finish college, to have a career and a family. Instead of doing what the comments told her to (ending her life) she chose to defy them and truly live.

Tears were running down my face as she asked the audience, "What defines you?"

Do our imperfect bodies define us? Does the world's opinion define us? Does fear define us?

"DARE TO BE BRAVE," she said; this woman who jokes about having large bins of Twinkies and Skittles in her college dorm room, because she's never been heavier than 64 pounds – so what does it matter? *This woman who said she may not be able to see out of one eye, but hey – then you only need half a prescription!*

I'm in my pajamas at three in the afternoon, weeping.

I was the pastor's kid who had head gear and braces, large plastic glasses and bangs, decked out in Northern Reflections clothing and starving herself to death.

I didn't eat because the world told me skinny was best. I got down to sixty pounds and the nurses said I should have died.

But I am alive.

Abundantly. Alive.

Every day we choose whether we believe what the world says about us, or what God says about us.

Every day we choose whether or not to serve fear, or Jesus. *Do we step on the scale for the tenth time,* or do we throw the scale in the garbage and forgive ourselves for last night's extra piece of cake?

Do we choose to look at how many followers we've gained or lost on social media, or do we pick up the Bible and read about who God says we are?

The world does not define me. My definition rests in One who knew me before I was born.

We've got one life friends.

Let's live it full – like Lizzie.

How do you define your worth? Is it based on what someone says about you? Or is it based on a deep intrinsic knowledge of how loved you are?

As women, we are often judged based on our appearance. How does this affect you personally?

What is the secret that Lizzie has discovered to finding confidence in her self-worth? Do you long to uncover the same secret?

Do you have any negative influences in your life which are keeping you from moving forward into your true identity? If so, are you willing to confront/remove them?

What unfulfilled dreams lie dormant in your heart? What is stopping you?

Chapter Fourteen

SPACE

• • • • • • • • • • • • • • • • • Lori Lara • • • • • • • • • • • • • • • • •

"People will forget what you said. People will forget what you did. But people will never forget how you made them feel."
— Maya Angelou

My husband and I were full time professionals for almost eight years before our first son was born. We both took care of cleaning the house, and when we walked out of a room, we were guaranteed it would remain as clean as it was when we left. Oh, the things we take for granted before having kids.

I worked in sales alongside my dad at his mortgage company, followed by five wonderful years as a salesperson for KFAX Radio. In both careers, my clients loved me, I got along well with my co-workers, and my bosses appreciated my ideas and dedicated work ethic. Everyone was happy with my work, affirming me often; and I was jazzed about taking care of their needs.

Lori, you're doing a great job. We appreciate you.

I had a loving husband, a quiet, perpetually clean home, and lots of professional affirmation.

Enter: baby, chaos, and what in the world happened to my house?

After giving birth, I very quickly became sleep-starved Zombie Mom. I made notes in the margin of my nursing schedule to track how much sleep I was losing each day (what can I say, Zombies have issues.) The 24/7 feed, burp, change, cry, cry, and cry-some-more routine was killing me. And when our second son came along, all my time was spent drowning in the urgency of newborn care while chasing a toddler who wanted nothing to do with nap time. I had zero time to even think about keeping our house clean.

Before becoming a mom, I read volumes of baby books to help us get ready for parenthood. I think someone ripped out important chapters of each book, because nothing prepared me for what was about to take over my home. Our peaceful sanctuary transformed into Baby Central complete with new tools and gadgets that promised to make life easier (monitors, changing table, diapers galore, baby wipes, bottles, baby swing, baby seat, breast pump, and a slew of lotions and ointments and oral drops to care for all the mysterious tummy problems, diaper rashes, and cracked nipples.) Baby gear littered every room in our house. I was working harder than I ever worked before, but my house was a mess and I had no affirmation.

The void spoke loudly. Lori, you're failing. No one appreciates you.

This feeling of failure drove me to my knees. I had achieved all my professional goals, but I was failing in the most important roles of my life—wife and mom. The clutter in the house, the thick layer of dust on everything, and the dirty bathrooms screamed that I was a mess.

After years of mommy guilt, I had a breakdown. In addition to the difficult adjustments of motherhood, I had deeper emotional issues that needed healing. Intensive counseling revealed that my self-esteem was rooted in performance people pleasing; that's why my messy house rocked my internal world so much. I felt others would judge me harshly, and I missed the external praises that helped me feel good about myself. When I discovered my greatest value comes from who I am to God - not how happy people are with me – I was able to gain a greater vision for myself, my family, and our home. This realization of my worth changed how I saw everything, including sticky floors and muddy fingerprints.

Our "space" is so much more than a clean, finely decorated house. We need to ask ourselves:

"What is the goal of my home?" And, "How well does it take care of the needs of each person living here?"

"Is my home an inspiring, safe place for my kids to grow and learn and make mistakes, or do they feel scared to finger paint on the kitchen table or break a dish?"

"Does my home inspire celebration and friendship, or do I stop inviting people over because I have dirty dishes in the sink and haven't vacuumed in weeks?"

If our highest goal is to create a warm and loving environment for our family, then having toys and stuffed animals and Play-Doh on the kitchen floor won't bother us as much; it will actually affirm us.

Right now our dining room table is scattered with books, old art projects that haven't yet found a home, a bag of colored pencils, and a stack of old newspapers that were never read. We have walking sticks, muddy shoes, and rusted scooters on our front porch.

Do I wish our house was tidier? You bet.

But because cleanliness isn't my highest priority, I can see the beauty in those messes. They reflect everything important to me: learning, creativity, play and the people I love most.

When our kids are grown up and someone asks them about their childhood home, I don't want them to say, "Oh, my mom was a frustrated, raving lunatic. But, boy – she sure kept a clean house."

No, thank you.

I'll want them to close their eyes and feel all the love I have for them beating right there in their hearts. And when life hits them hard (and we know it will), I want the memory of our home to always be their safe place to fall, long after they stop living with us.

Moms, one day we'll sit back and enjoy our tranquil and spotless homes again. But deep down, as we admire our sparkling windows – a part of us will miss those muddy handprints.

· · · · · · · · · · · · · *Reflection Questions* · · · · · · · · · · · · ·

Does my home reflect my family's highest priorities?

What can I do to make my space special?

In the future, what do I want my grown up kids to remember most about our home?

Do I need to see my space/messes differently?

What unrealistic expectations do I need to let go of so I can enjoy this stage of mothering?

Chapter Fifteen

RAISING ADULTS

• • • • • • • • • • • • • • • • Mandy Arioto • • • • • • • • • • • • • •

"A weird contradiction occurs in parenting: we want children to be a certain way when they are young – compliant, basically – but then we want the complete opposite for them as adults."
- M. Arioto

I don't like being told what to do. I know this is not a great trait to admit to, but I am all about full disclosure. I think it is the stubborn Irish streak that I inherited from my Grandpa Mac. If you ever meet my brother, you will learn that he inherited even more of it than I did. This is something that seriously irritates me and makes me a little jealous all at the same time. You see, the degree of my brother's stubbornness in some way makes him charming. He is the one at the party dancing on the table while the rest of us circle him to see what he'll do next. He is willful and headstrong - and people love him for it. I, on the other hand, got the more cerebral version of stubbornness. It is the less enviable version where I am compelled to fight for the underdog and stand up to old people in my neighborhood who yell at my kids for playing 'too loud.' Is it even possible to play too loudly? (See what I mean?)

My stubborn streak also carries over into following directions and recipes. They just seem too inflexible, too restrictive. I like to view a recipe more as a good jumping off point than a rigid formula. I justify this thinking by rationalizing that it frees me up to be creative. That somehow this need to be free from boundaries is actually a good thing. The truth is, this way of thinking has gotten me into trouble more than a few times. My kids beg to hear stories of when I was a kid, and my stubborn streak got the best of me.

It is strange to have kids, because as they get older you begin to see yourself in them. The things that you like about yourself you also like about them. The things you would rather have kept to yourself are passed on, and it makes you blush like a ruddy-cheeked, kilted Highlander to see those traits arise in your offspring. It becomes inevitable that you have to face your delicate traits, because they interact with you in a little fleshy body every day. In walks my stubbornness, dressed in a pink night gown with beautiful blond hair and stunning blue eyes. A little girl who is precocious and intuitive and stubborn – just like her mom.

Occasionally I struggle with my precocious children. These strong willed people I share a home and a life with. When they ask me unending questions and fight about how unjust it is that someone got a piece of candy cane that was three millimeters bigger than their brother and sister. Or when one of them stands up to their teacher who said unkind words and I get a call from the principal, it is those moments when I momentarily wish they were less. Less passionate. Less opinionated. Less feisty.

And then I come to my senses. I remember that my job as a mom is way bigger than raising compliant children. *My job is to raise remarkable adults.*

A weird contradiction occurs in parenting: we want children to be a certain way when they are young – compliant, basically – but then we want the complete opposite for them as adults. When they hit eighteen we want them to switch from compliance to assertiveness. To stand up for what they believe, to have a voice of their own and to be creative enough to solve any problem they bump up against. This is so weird, right?

I was talking with my brother (that's right, the one with the great dance moves) last week about how frustrating it was as a kid because he would get terrible grades in math. He could figure out the correct answer but never could show his work on the paper like he was supposed to. His teachers never gave credit for using alternative ways to find the right answer. My parents didn't make a big deal about it because they were more impressed that he knew the answers and found them in ways no one else saw. Isn't that the goal of raising human beings? To help them see problems in the world and find uncommon ways to solve them?

I think the issue is that sometimes as parents it is easier to raise compliant kids than it is to raise exceptional adults. Because often times the qualities that make up extraordinary adults are difficult to manage in children.

So what does raising remarkable adults look like? Maybe it looks a little bit like:

Sharing Family Stories
Marshall Duke, a psychologist at Emory University was asked to research stress and resiliency in kids. His research found that kids who know a lot about their families tend to do better when they face challenges. Dr. Duke developed something called the "Do You Know?" scale, which asked children to answer 20 questions. Examples included: Do you know where your grandparents

grew up? Do you know where your mom and dad went to high school? Do you know where your parents met? Do you know an illness or something really terrible that happened in your family? Do you know the story of your birth? The overwhelming conclusion was that the more children knew about their family's history, the stronger their sense of control over their lives, the higher their self-esteem and the more successfully they believed their families functioned. The "Do You Know?" scale turned out to be the best single predictor of children's emotional health and happiness well into adulthood.

The most healthful family story is called the oscillating family narrative and goes something like this, "We've had ups and downs in our family. We built a family business. Your grandfather was a pillar of the community. But we also had setbacks. You had an uncle who was once arrested. We had a house burn down. Your father lost a job. But no matter what happened, we always stuck together as a family." Dr. Duke says that children who have the most self-confidence heading into adulthood are the ones who have a strong "intergenerational self." They know they belong to something bigger than themselves.

Being On the Same Team
We have a sign that hangs on the wall near our table that says, "We are all in this together." It is a reminder that we are on the same team, and that we will always have each other's best interest in mind.

My husband Joe's Dad said something to him that forever changed their relationship. When Joe was little, his Dad told him that he would always try to say yes. This meant that anytime Joe wanted to go somewhere with friends or asked for more time to get his chores finished or asked for him to play, Joe knew that his Dad would always try to say yes. That didn't mean he always did, but simply understanding that his Dad wanted to say yes made the no's more palatable.

Sometimes a parent-child relationship evolves into "them against us" or a "battle of wills." By letting our kids know that we are for them and in it together, we can eliminate the power struggle. We become a team. Our kids learn that we are watching out for each other, and even though we may not always get what we want – everyone still wants the best for the other person.

Fighting for a Cause
One of my favorite writers is a guy named Viktor Frankel. He survived a Nazi concentration camp and came to be a world renowned psychiatrist. He says that "we aren't designed to spend too much time thinking about ourselves, we are healthier when we are distracted by a noble cause." What if we talk to our

kids about injustice and asked them for ideas on how to solve it? I am continually impressed with the wisdom and compassion that kids display when given the opportunity. Build a house for Habitat for Humanity, or visit an orphanage in Mexico and let your kids play with the children who live there. We took our kids to an orphanage in Mexico one summer and they drew in chalk and ate hotdogs with all of the kids. I am pretty sure they had just as great a time as the kids we visited. *When we weave opportunities for our kids to focus on the needs of other, we also help them to better understand the heart of God.* And as God's hands and feet in the world, we empower our kids to summon the courage to fight injustice – courage they might not have developed otherwise.

Eating Together

Hold onto your hats because you are not going to believe the power of food around a table. There has been a recent wave of research that shows that *children who eat dinner with their families are less likely to drink, smoke, do drugs, get pregnant, commit suicide, and develop eating disorders.* All that from a shared lasagna. Pretty impressive. Additional research tells us that children who enjoy family meals have larger vocabularies, better manners, healthier diets, and higher self-esteem.

The most comprehensive survey done on this topic came out of the University of Michigan where they examined how American children spent their time between 1981 and 1997. They discovered that *the amount of time children spent eating meals at home was the single biggest predictor of better academic achievement and fewer behavioral problems.* Mealtime was more influential than time spent in school, studying, attending religious services or playing sports.

It's pretty remarkable that sharing food around a table can have this big of an impact on kids' well-being. I personally am relieved, because I can do this. It may be pizza that I pick up on the way home from work, but eating around a table and talking seems like just about the best way to end a day.

Paying Attention to Birthrights

The Bible talks a lot about birth rights. It is the idea that we have inherent giftings that have been woven into our souls from the beginning of time. The interesting thing is that most times these birth right gifts show up when we are young. Loving to paint or banging on a piano, making cardboard boxes into fantastical creations, being a leader on the playground or standing up to bullies. When we see each of our children's unique gifts and nurture that, we are helping them own their God- given birth rights.

Too often as adults we forego our birthrights for more predictable or profitable ways to fill our days. How sad that we forego what is meant to give us more life for things that may pay the bills, but leave us feeling like we aren't fulfilling what we were put on the earth to do. A gift that we give each adult we raise is to nurture their gifts when they are young so they have the freedom to follow their birthright as adults.

Listening and Looking

I love this quote by Catherine M. Wallace:

"Listen earnestly to anything [your children] want to tell you, no matter what. If you don't listen eagerly to the little stuff when they are little, they won't tell you the big stuff when they are big, because to them all of it has always been big stuff."

It seems to me that one of the greatest gifts that we can give our kids is to look them in the eye and really listen. So often days go by and I realize that we have been circling around one another, eating meals and doing life near one another – but we haven't really seen each other. Have you ever sat with someone and truly felt seen and heard? It is perhaps the one thing that reminds me that I am a valuable soul rather than a performing being. When we show our kids that they are worthy of our attention, we gift them with a sense of value. And when they feel valuable, they grow into adults who will extend that same gift to our grandchildren. It is a generational blessing.

So friends, let's celebrate the stubborn spark of wildness in the creatures in our homes. The uncommon kids who ask uncomfortable questions and solve problems in ways we never would have considered. The world needs more rebels and dreamers, unique problem solvers who grow up believing they are responsible for sharing their gifts with the world. And instead of going with the flow, playing quietly and showing their work – this generation of kids will stand up to injustice and uplift humanity for generations to come.

Blessed are the stubborn rule breakers, because they will inherit the freedom to play as loudly as they want and never be thwarted by neighbors who have forgotten how to play. Amen.

• • • • • • • • • • • • •*Reflection Questions*• • • • • • • • • • • •

What traits do you notice in your children that were passed down by you?

Do you make it a point to share family stories with your kids? Which stories come to mind that you could share with them?

Are you and your child(ren) on the same team? What can you do to be on the same side and tone down the battle of wills?

Have you observed any natural gifts or talents in your children? What are they, and how can you nurture their gifts?

When your child tugs on your sleeve or comes running to show you something so important, do you really listen? What can you do this week to be a better listener for your son or daughter?

Chapter Sixteen

THE ADOPTION ALTERNATIVE

• • • • • • • • • • • • • • • Jen Hatmaker • • • • • • • • • • • • • • •

"We care for orphans not because we are rescuers, but because we are the rescued." - David Platt

A Note from MOPS:

Here at MOPS, we count Jen Hatmaker among our favorite voices; and lucky us! – she is also a friend. So when we asked her to share her wisdom and passion for reaching out to impact the least of these – orphans around the world, she was more than happy to lend her voice to this book. Why talk about the plight of orphaned children and struggling families in a book about flourishing? Because MOPS is all about reaching out, and what better way to leave your mark on this world than by helping moms, families and children in need to flourish. Becoming a mother makes us part of something bigger, and we have an opportunity to help change the story for other moms. Learning some of the best ways to lift up moms and littles right next door or halfway around the world is a great way to get started.

• •

Let's talk about children – beautiful, potential-filled little souls around the world – who happen also to be orphans. And if we're going to talk about the orphan crisis, let's get our numbers straight. There are an estimated 153 million kids who've lost only one parent ("single-orphaned"), so the term "orphan" is somewhat misleading. Around 18 million kids are double-orphans, yet still most of those are absorbed into extended families and local communities.

Unicef estimates around 2 million children in institutional care (some single-, some double-orphaned), although that number is admittedly low due to under-reporting and lack of reliable data from every country. Nearly half are in Central and Eastern Europe and neighboring Commonwealth of Independent States. Most of these kids are not adoptable, either because they live in a closed country or they lack the necessary documentation for international adoption. In the US, there are 104,000 children in foster care currently waiting for an adoptive home (parental rights severed), with another 300,000 or so needing temporary placement.

International adoption has steadily declined in recent years, with 8668 children adopted by Americans in 2012 (but 51,000 kids adopted through the foster system!) So even if we doubled the number of reported institutionalized kids to 4 million, absorbing some of the unreported children into the statistic, international adoption by US citizens provides permanent homes for 0.002% of them.

1 child out of every 461.

Those are terrible odds. *Clearly, if we are truly concerned about orphan care, international adoption simply cannot be where we concentrate all our efforts.* It leaves too many children behind. It isn't even remotely comprehensive, nor does it affect the millions of families on the brink of poverty-induced relinquishment. It is very good news for a very small percentage of genuinely orphaned children, but it doesn't even scratch the surface of the crisis, will never address the root issues of disparity and oppression, and exists as a possible answer on the back end of a tragedy, not the front.

Therefore, we must turn our eyes to the orphaned (or nearly-orphaned) outside of adoption as well, as this is where the bulk of vulnerable children and families are located.

It is unacceptable that poverty makes orphans. That is a gross injustice at the root of these astronomical numbers. *If you must relinquish your child because you cannot feed, educate, or care for him, the international community should rise up and wage war against that inequity.* Every family deserves basic human rights, and I should not get to raise your child simply because I can feed him and you can't.

To that end, what better response than working to preserve (or reunite) first families where poverty or disempowerment is an orphan-maker? *Preventing or repairing a tragedy of this magnitude is holy work.* When we come alongside our brothers and sisters vulnerable to economic despair, empowering and equipping them to raise their own children, we partake in something sacred.

There are fundamental building blocks of community development that provide first families the tools to parent and thrive:
- Prenatal/maternal health
- Basic health care/immunizations
- Clean water

- Education for all kids, especially girls
- Child sponsorship
- Birth control/family planning education
- Community education directed at men re: valuing women and children
- Sustainable employment
- Microfinance
- Business training
 Drying up the donation pipeline (gifts that help instead of hurt)
- Suitable housing
- Agricultural finance
- Reforestation
- Supporting local churches as distribution and development centers

The connective thread between these social constructs and orphans is monumental. *Hear this: if you work toward any of the above-mentioned initiatives, you are absolutely protecting children, refusing to "grind the faces of the poor." THIS COUNTS.* For example, in Haiti last fall with Help One Now, Chris Marlow explained the underbelly of donations. After years of exporting subsidized US rice to alleviate hunger in Haiti, virtually all the local rice farmers were driven out of business and the entire economy was undermined. The leap to orphanhood is so short from there.

Help One Now approached the struggling rice farmers and asked if sponsoring their children would help them regain stable footing. Temporarily taking on the financial burden of school fees, uniforms, and two meals a day for their kids relieved the pressure, freed up income to rebuild, and allowed them to keep their families intact, as their children were on the brink of relinquishment, poverty the only catalyst.

A growing body of global research confirms that where women and children are valued and educated, poverty is mitigated. Throwing our weight behind initiatives that empower women and educate children is one the single most effective ways to affect the orphan crisis, as it lifts entire communities out of poverty, alters the ethos of regional patriarchy, and serves as orphan prevention. (If you haven't read Half the Sky, I cannot recommend it highly enough. Their research behind the oppression and empowerment of women is a marvel.)

Business initiatives that train and employ vulnerable adults have clear and lasting implications for family preservation, too. With organizations like Noonday employing women in nine different countries, and TechnoServe which provides free business consulting services in developing countries, and Making Cents International, a nonprofit in Washington that creates entrepreneurship courses for the disadvantaged and trains locals to teach them, cycles of poverty are broken and the economic stimulus affects entire communities.

What might just sound like community development actually has massive impact on the number of poverty-induced orphans created. These efforts fortify orphan prevention, and they can provide the impetus for family reunification. *These initiatives lay the axe at the root of the tree, offering front-end solutions and sustainable enterprises without sacrificing dignity, children, or hope.*

Closer to the bulls-eye, we can support organizations committed to reunification (if healthy and possible) for children already relinquished. Heroes like my friends Jimmy and Rachel Gross with No Ordinary Love Ministries in Ethiopia work tirelessly to this end. Or let's look for organizations like ReUnite (with WACIA: Women and Children in Africa) who work toward orphan resettlement in Uganda. People are quietly working in every country to strengthen indigenous families, support birth parents and protect children.

Domestically, I cannot recommend Safe Families for Children enough, which offers sanctuary to thousands of children, minimizing the risk for abuse or neglect and giving birth parents the time and tools they need to help their families thrive. The ultimate goal is to strengthen and support parents so they can become safe for their own children, fostering a close working relationships between Safe Families, the local church, the referring organization, and the birth parents.

Far from ideal, *we must also consider bolstering the quality and structures of group homes and orphanages.* Research makes it crystal clear that children thrive in families but suffer emotionally, cognitively, and physically in institutional settings. Ideally, every child should be in a family. Realistically, adoption and reunification do not even remotely reach far enough, so we must also consider best-case scenarios for children that will never be placed within a family.

For example, Help One Now is building Ferrier Village in Haiti, small, family-oriented homes for girls aging out of orphanages as young as 13. Each home has 3-4 girls and a house mom or house parents. The alternative is inevitable trafficking or homelessness. The Miracle Foundation renovates and restructures existing orphanages in rural India with measurable, scalable interventions that guard against corruption and focus on the needs of the whole child, transforming institutional orphanages into stable, loving, nurturing homes where children can thrive. With over 25 million estimated orphans in India and less than 1000 adopted last year, we simply must consider initiatives like The Miracle Foundation who are addressing the needs of the masses.

A crisis of this magnitude is going to take us all - all the mamas, all the daddies, all the countries, all the workers. Some of us will raise the money, some will raise awareness, and some will raise the kids. Certain families will rally from here, and other families will pack up and move to vulnerable countries and do the work. Some of us will be starters, some executers, some funders, some visionaries. *We collectively must insist on helping and not hurting, refusing to discredit the weak links in the system and instead insist on shoring them up.*

We have to dig deep and reject the notion that Americans know best, are best, are better. We have to listen to dissenting voices and carefully assess, prioritizing first families, first cultures, first countries whenever possible. We move forward as if our goal was no orphans ever, setting aside our agendas, however altruistic. *Our standard operating procedure must always include Being Good News: good for children, good for birth mamas, good for the poor, good for other countries and cultures.*

Within that framework, we're all going to have to fight like hell together. In the Old Testament, the Hebrew word for "justice" translates: "to set right." *May we be a people who bravely commit to set the wrongs right,* because being too poor to parent isn't right. Being too sick to parent isn't right. Being abandoned or abused isn't right. Being discarded because of special needs or gender isn't right. Being manipulated into relinquishment isn't right. Wasting away unloved in an orphanage isn't right. Being trapped in cycles of poverty isn't right.

May we apply the same standards we insist on for our families to all families, unwilling to accept disparity and injustice. *I'll play my note and you'll play yours, and by themselves, they'll be sort of one-dimensional, but together they will create a song that sounds like freedom for the captives, liberty for the oppressed, and the beautiful sound of chains breaking everywhere.*

AUTHOR BIOS

Mandy Arioto

Mandy Arioto has three kids, two dogs and married her husband in spite of the fact that he used the cheesiest pick up line ever to ask her out. She and her husband recently moved from Southern California to Denver so that their kids could learn how to make snow angels and because they believe in adventures. Before joining MOPS, Mandy was a preaching pastor at MOSAIC in San Diego. She is widely accepted as a relationship expert, and has been featured on MSN, theknot.com, thenest.com and FOX. She and her husband are in the throes of raising three young kids to be adventurous, tender-hearted world changers. *She has her first book coming out in April of 2016! Yay! Get more details on where you can pick it up at www.mandyarioto.com.* p.s. Mandy's personal cell phone number is found in the pages of this book, so give her a call to chat. Or you can follow her on Instagram and she will follow you right back.

Lori Lara

Lori Lara is a writer, blogger, and black-belt martial arts instructor. By sharing her raw story of healing through depression and post-traumatic stress, Lori is passionate about encouraging others through the hard times of life. She believes the joys and struggles of motherhood are meant to be shared, and no matter what our weaknesses, God has a good plan for each of us. In addition to her blog (lorilara.com), she's co-authored several books: Hope in the Mourning (Zondervan 2013), The Multitasking Mom's Survival Guide (Chicken Soup for the Soul 2013), and Reboot Your Life (Chicken Soup for the Soul 2014). Lori lives in Northern California with her husband Robert and their two sons. You can email her at lori@lorilaraphotography.com.

Emily T. Wierenga

Emily T. Wierenga is an award-winning journalist, blogger, commissioned artist and columnist, and the author of five books including the memoir Atlas Girl: Finding Home in the Last Place I Thought to Look (Baker Books). All proceeds from Atlas Girl benefit Emily's non-profit, The Lulu Tree. She lives in Alberta, Canada with her husband and two sons. For more info, please visit www. emilywierenga.com. Find her on Twitter or Facebook.

Jen Hatmaker

Jen Hatmaker and her husband Brandon live in Austin, TX where they lead Austin New Church and raise their brood. They pioneered Restore Austin, connecting churches to local and global non-profits for the spiritual and social renewal of Austin and beyond. Jen speaks at events all around the country. She is the author of nine books and Bible studies, including Interrupted and 7: An Experimental Mutiny Against Excess. Jen and Brandon have five children, including a son and daughter adopted from Ethiopia. Check out her ministry, schedule, and blog at www. jenhatmaker.com.

Ways I Will

CELEBRATE LAVISHLY

EMBRACE REST

· ·

· ·